To   Su

From

Love Ali
X X

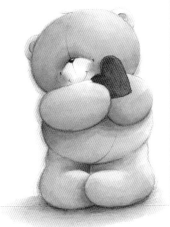

You are

everywhere

The air is changed
with your presence –
everywhere.

Falling in love
is the greatest excitement
of all.

Beauty and joy
seem to shine through –
because I am in love.

You are in the room,
and all else is forgotten.

And we are held in a silence
of our own.

All the world has changed

I am dizzy with the thought of you.
I think I am bewitched...

Love is...
moonlight
and romance
and roses.

Magic

Love...
with all its heartache and confusion.

Only

I mean to think of other things,
things I should do or write or say.
But all that's in my mind is you.

To fall in love
is to curl in an empty chair.
Is to watch at the window.
Is to wait for the telephone to ring.
Is to think of you every moment
you're not here.

Learning
to love

Let us learn to love slowly,
a smile, a touch of the hand,
a gentleness,
a quiet blossoming.

Love is when you can spend
a day doing nothing in particular –
and be supremely happy.

It is not passion
that is the great delight.
It is the first shared smile,
the quiet talk as you walk.
The retreating of the world
of sight and sound,
that leaves you in
a silence of your own.

Here's your letter –
read again and again. It tides
me over until you come.

You have invaded my thoughts.
Everything I think or do turns upon you.
I see you everywhere.

It's love!